Co-occurring Disord...

# UNDERSTANDING DEPRESSION AND ADDICTION

Revised

Katie Evans, Ph.D.

HAZELDEN®

FORMERLY THE DUAL DIAGNOSIS SERIES

Hazelden
Center City, Minnesota 55012-0176

1-800-328-9000
1-651-213-4590 (Fax)
www.hazelden.org

©1991, 2003 by Hazelden Foundation
All rights reserved. First edition 1991
Second edition 2003
Printed in the United States of America

To request permission, write to
Permissions Coordinator, Hazelden
P.O. Box 176, Center City, MN 55012-0176.
To purchase additional copies of this publication, call
1-800-328-9000 or 1-651-213-4000.

ISBN: 1-59285-011-1

**Editor's note**

This material was written to educate individuals about chemical dependency and mental illness. It is not intended as a substitute for professional medical or psychiatric care.

Any stories or case studies that may be used in this material are composites of many individuals. Names and details have been changed to protect identities.

Permission to reprint the Twelve Steps does not mean that Alcoholics Anonymous has reviewed or approved the contents of this publication, nor that AA agrees with the views expressed herein. AA is a program of recovery from alcoholism only. Use of the Twelve Steps in connection with programs and activities which are patterned after AA but which address other problems does not imply otherwise.

Cover design by Lightbourne
Interior design by Lightbourne

# CONTENTS

# INTRODUCTION

This pamphlet is for you, the person suffering from the disease of chemical dependency and the disease of major depression.

It may surprise you to learn that major depression is a disease just like alcoholism, diabetes, or cancer. Maybe you're reading this because you think, or someone close to you thinks, that you're depressed. Perhaps a qualified professional such as a psychiatrist, psychologist, or mental health nurse practitioner has diagnosed your condition as suffering from a major depression. Or you may be one of the thousands of recovering alcoholics or recovering addicts who are working a Twelve Step program but continue to suffer from feelings of sadness, extreme guilt, hopelessness, and helplessness well into sobriety. You may even have contemplated suicide while maintaining sobriety, thinking that the program is just not working for you. You may have found the spiritual part of the program difficult to get.

The purpose of this pamphlet is to give you information about your dual diseases of major depression and chemical dependency and to offer some practical suggestions that can enhance the quality of your recovery from both disorders.

Throughout the pamphlet, the term "dual diagnosis" or "dual disorders" refers to two coexisting problems.

The dual disorders discussed in this pamphlet are major depression and chemical dependency. This pamphlet will not discuss which came first, the depression or the addiction. This question is as confusing as the chicken or the egg question. People with major depression can become chemically dependent and chemically dependent people can suffer from major depression.

Depression is common when first entering recovery. Addictions wear down the body, mind, and spirit and make life unmanageable. Trying to control the uncontrollable adds its own burden. Ironically, some depression is actually helpful because it can give individuals a glimpse through their denial and give them the motivation to enter recovery. A clear look at your true self in the mirror can be most difficult to accept. The pain can motivate people to recover. (Why change if everything is "just fine"?)

Depression in early recovery is common. After all, who wouldn't be depressed to learn that he or she is an addict and needs to change? You may discover that your behavior hurts yourself as well as others—a situation you face when beginning recovery. Family problems, work problems, and legal and financial problems are common for those addicted to chemicals. Being confronted by these harsh realities can be overwhelming. Depression in the first few weeks of sobriety is common and should be expected. It usually lifts, however, within several weeks of detoxification and of completing quality treatment and staying on the path of recovery.

This pamphlet will focus on the illness that lasts beyond the weeks and months of early sobriety and while you are working a program of recovery: major depression. This depression can dilute the quality of your recovery, lead to a relapse, or even make suicide seem attractive. This pamphlet is not a quick fix or a substitute for professional assistance but a source of information and tools that you may find helpful in your recovery from both disorders. A worksheet on page 33, "Coming to Know Your Disorders," will help you define your own situation and attitudes.

By learning how to "work a program" for both your chemical dependency and your major depression, you will begin to experience the serenity that others working a Twelve Step program have experienced as well as the promises that the Big Book of Alcoholics Anonymous (AA) offers. You, too, will find happiness far beyond your imagination.

# ONE

# THE DISEASES OF ADDICTION AND MAJOR DEPRESSION

Both chemical dependency and major depression are diseases, and certain steps are necessary for recovery. Table 1, "Comparison of the Diseases of Chemical Dependency and Major Depression," on page 11, outlines the causes, symptoms, and recovery program for these two disorders. Table 2, "How Depression and Addiction Progress and How You Can Recover," on page 13, outlines the progression and the process of recovery for both diseases. You may want to review them now and again after you read the rest of this section.

## Chemical Dependency

Introducing into your body a substance with potential for abuse, such as alcohol, can begin a process of change in brain chemistry and function that results in addiction. If you have a family history of alcoholism or other addictions, you are at greater risk for this process to occur. Tolerance, which is the need to take increasing amounts of a substance to achieve the same effects, is one sign that the physical process of addiction has begun. Another sign is withdrawal—uncomfortable and perhaps even fatal physical, mental, and emotional problems that can develop after you stop using alcohol or drugs.

The key symptoms of the full-fledged disease of chemical dependency include loss of control over our life and continued use of the substance despite problems in living that our use causes. Perhaps you have tried to cut down or quit, but cannot. Or maybe you find that you continually drink or use more than planned. Perhaps you're taking more and more of the addictive substance for longer periods of time and using more kinds of the substances. This is known as *progression*. Or maybe you find you have become preoccupied with use so that use becomes the focus of your life, excluding other people and activities. Other symptoms of the disease of addiction include such negative consequences as continued use of drugs or alcohol despite liver damage, severe fights at home, getting fired from a job, legal charges for driving under the influence, or the loss of all faith and hope.

Denial is an important part of the disease of chemical dependency. You undoubtedly experienced denial prior to entering recovery. You have a disease that tells you that you don't have a disease!

Chemical dependency is a progressive disease—it gets worse with time if left untreated. It is a chronic disease with no cure. But you can experience a remission. Recovery starts with abstinence. Your attendance at Alcoholics Anonymous or similar self-help groups and your work with a sponsor or support person provide the help and guidance necessary to promote recovery. Working the Twelve Steps can lead you to accept the disease, repair the emotional and spiritual damage caused by your drinking and using, and, last but not least, help you experience personal growth nothing short of a spiritual awakening.

## Major Depression

It is important to understand that major depression is a disease like chemical dependency. Just as with chemical dependency, if you suffer from major depression you are sick getting well, not bad getting good. You are not responsible for having major depression; experiencing this illness does not mean you have a character defect. However, you are responsible for recovering from this illness.

Sometimes major depression comes out of the blue. But generally the experience of severe stress—for example, the death of a spouse, the loss of a job, or having a serious physical illness diagnosed—can trigger depression. The experience of ongoing stresses such as fights with your spouse, work problems, or a serious, chronic illness can also cause major depression. Even seemingly happy events like retirement, the birth of a child, or moving to a new location for job purposes are stressful and can begin a downward spiral into major depression. Having a family history of depression and suicide can increase the chances of developing this disorder.

There are important signs of the physical process of major depression that you may have experienced. One sign is a big change in your appetite. Another sign is prolonged disturbance of sleep patterns (especially waking up early and being unable to fall back to sleep). Loss of pleasure in usually enjoyable events and a blue mood that is worse in the morning than later in the day are also signs of this process.

There are other signs of major depression. You may find that you feel very sad, "down," or irritable for days or weeks at a time. You may have serious trouble concentrating and making decisions or constantly feel guilty and overwhelmed. You may find yourself doing less and less at home and work. Perhaps you have become withdrawn and isolated and no longer enjoy spending time with family or friends. Perhaps you feel fatigued and apathetic and on a bad day you can hardly get out of bed to go to work or do household chores. You might even think of killing yourself.

A hopeless/helpless mind-set is a key symptom of the disease of major depression. You may have begun to think that everything is always going to go poorly, that somehow all this bad stuff is your fault, that you are a thoroughly bad person and there is nothing you can do to make any of it better. Others may point out your good features to you and try to talk you out of your negative thinking, but it doesn't help. Your persistent negative thinking is an important symptom of your major depression. When these dark days hit, it seems they will last forever, while the good days seem fleeting.

## Mary's Story

Mary had experienced periods of depression during her drinking days. These down times would last for several weeks. She found that during these periods she drank even more than usual to try to drown out the black spells. Shortly after celebrating her third year of continuous sobriety in Alcoholics Anonymous, Mary suffered a stroke. She lost all movement in her arms and legs and was hospitalized for two weeks. She then returned home in a wheelchair. Mary felt exhausted taking even a few steps, yet she knew she must push herself if she were going to recover. But she found she just didn't have the energy to push herself. She felt tired, helpless, and hopeless. Mary was struggling with her faith. She was mad at God for letting all this happen to her.

Mary began to doubt that she would ever be "normal" again. Friends in AA tried to remind her to take it "one day at a time," but she began to lose hope and faith. Over the next month her depression deepened.

She began to wonder if her Twelve Step program was working and whether she had the ability to work a program. Mary was suffering from the disease of depression.

## Grief and Loss

Most people who enter recovery from addiction find that they have unresolved grief and loss issues. Perhaps it is the grief and loss of the life they might have had if they had not taken that first pill, fix, or drink. Others have drunk and used through the death of family members and friends. Yet others never grieved the loss of broken relationships because they used chemicals to avoid the grief.

It is perfectly normal, and usually expected, that most alcoholics and addicts will experience a period of grief and loss of the drug and/or drink. Saying good-bye to the old friend, which helped them survive life on life's terms, and to think of a clean and sober life ahead is difficult and involves grief and loss.

Grief and loss is a process, which many of us tried to avoid. The stages of grief are

1. shock and denial

2. sadness

3. anger

4. examination

5. acceptance of the loss

These phases of grief happen gradually and you may find yourself spiraling up and down through this process. Grief and loss is *different from the disease of depression*. It does not require medication. Counseling and support is helpful, but as it is said, time heals all wounds. Work on your grief and loss issues with your therapist, sponsor, and by working the Steps. This, too, will and shall pass. Time takes time.

## Recovery Is Possible

Depression during active drinking or using drugs is common—so is depression in the first three or four weeks of sobriety as the body readjusts and you begin to grapple with the consequences of your chemical use. But if you continue to experience lasting symptoms of serious depression several weeks after detoxification, while you are clean and sober, you probably have major depression and would find a dual recovery program helpful.

Your recovery from major depression can start with building and using a sound support system. Increasing your physical, social, and recreational activities can help to promote recovery. Working on positive thinking can lead to a more realistic and hopeful mind-set. In many cases, taking antidepressant medication can relieve some of the symptoms of depression and make the other recovery steps possible. Therapy with a qualified professional can also be helpful.

Following these suggestions can feel extremely overwhelming to a person who can barely get out of bed in the morning. Suffering from either the disease of chemical addiction or major depression can prove stressful and problematic for you. Suffering from both diseases can pose a difficult challenge at a time when simply getting dressed in the morning requires a maximum effort. But recovery from both diseases is possible. Understanding that you are suffering from coexisting disorders is the beginning of your journey to recovery. The next section of this pamphlet discusses action steps you can take to begin working a combined program.

# Summary

1. Major depression and chemical dependency are diseases; they are not signs of poor self-control or weak character.

2. Both diseases have key symptoms. For chemical dependency, the symptoms are loss of control and continued use despite negative consequences such as medical and financial problems or conflict with others. For major depression, the symptoms are a deeply sad mood and loss of interest or pleasure in all activities, persisting for several weeks, and feelings of hopelessness.

3. People in recovery who experience symptoms of depression for several weeks can benefit from a recovery program for depression.

Table 1

| COMPARISON OF THE DISEASES OF CHEMICAL DEPENDENCY AND MAJOR DEPRESSION | | |
|---|---|---|
| **Factor** | **Chemical Dependency** | **Major Depression** |
| *Causes* | • alcohol and drug use<br>• changes in brain chemistry and function<br>• heredity | • stress and grief and loss of relationships and ability to use chemicals<br>• changes in brain chemistry and function<br>• heredity |

Table 1 *(continued)*

| Factor | Chemical Dependency | Major Depression |
|--------|---------------------|------------------|
| *Symptoms* | • tolerance, withdrawal, progression<br>• loss of control of substance use and behavior<br>• continued use despite negative consequences<br>• physical, interpersonal, social, occupational, spiritual problems<br>• hospitalization, incarceration, insanity, death<br>• denial | • disturbance of appetite and sleep, decrease in energy level<br>• sad or irritable mood<br>• loss of pleasure or interest in most enjoyable activities<br>• physical, interpersonal, social, occupational, spiritual problems<br>• hospitalization, psychosis, thoughts of suicide<br>• helpless/hopeless mind-set<br>• loss of faith |
| *Recovery Program* | • abstinence<br>• Alcoholics Anonymous/Narcotics Anonymous attendance<br>• assistance from sponsor<br>• Twelve Step work | • social support<br>• increased activity level<br>• antidepressant medication and psychotherapy<br>• work on spiritual program |

## Table 2

## How Depression and Addiction Progress and How You Can Recover

**Drug Use Spiral**
- increased tolerance
- blackouts
- feelings of guilt
- loss of control
- lying about use
- sexual problems
- promises to change
- family problems
- work or school problems
- unreasonable anger
- legal problems
- decrease in tolerance
- increased use to maintain high
- chemical stops working
- admits defeat

**Depression Spiral**
- feeling blue
- increased sadness
- feelings of guilt
- confusion
- change of appetite
- sleep problems
- sexual problems
- family problems
- work or school problems
- agitation and irritation
- health problems
- feelings of impending doom
- severe depression
- thoughts of suicide
- suicide attempt

**Depression Recovery**
- sense of purpose and serenity
- contentment in sobriety
- restored confidence of employers
- family relations improve
- increased social and recreational activity
- begins positive thinking
- sleep begins to improve
- begins to work program
- accepts disease of depression

**Alcohol and Drug Recovery**
- attends to personal appearance
- appreciation of real values
- rebirth of ideals
- new interests develop
- adjustments to family needs
- return of self-esteem
- diminishing fears of the future
- diet improves
- onset of hope
- attends Alcoholics Anonymous/ Narcotics Anonymous
- positive thinking begins
- begins to work a program
- accepts disease of addiction
- honest desire for help

**Treatment**

# TWO

# WORKING A COMBINED PROGRAM

This section discusses in some detail the elements of working a combined program of recovery for your coexisting diseases of chemical dependency and major depression.

Your recovery from chemical dependency requires that you accept the disease of addiction and abstain from mood-altering chemicals. It involves attending Twelve Step meetings, getting a sponsor, working the Twelve Steps, and improving your physical health. Recovery from major depression also requires that you accept the disease. You must build a support system, increase your pleasurable activities, and think constructively. You may need psychotherapy to help develop positive thinking and improve your self-esteem and medication to correct a biochemical imbalance that contributes to your depression.

## Acceptance

Accepting that you have the diseases of chemical dependency and major depression is fundamental. Without this acceptance, you are likely to remain trapped in the notion that you are at fault and that you could get better if only you tried hard enough to make yourself feel better or to control your use of substances. Review the symptoms already discussed (page 12) and see how they apply to you. Listen to the opinions of your friends, family, and counselor. Ask yourself whether the solutions you have tried have been successful. Accepting your dual diseases is the first step in working your recovery program—a path that can lead you to a quality of life you never imagined possible.

## Abstinence

Abstinence is vital. You must be physically free from addictive chemicals. Using alcohol or other addictive chemicals will make both diseases worse and prevent the process of recovery from beginning. Without abstinence you will continue to have physical problems, including an imbalanced biochemistry. Your mood will continue to worsen and you will find fewer and fewer activities pleasurable. You will become less able to control your use of chemicals and you will experience the negative bodily, mental, emotional, and spiritual consequences of your use. This, in turn, will intensify your depression. Denial and negative thinking will increase. Only abstinence will help you to develop new solutions to old problems. As will be explained in more detail, taking antidepressant medication does not violate abstinence because this medication is not addictive.

## An Active Program

Working an active recovery program is crucial. Just as your diseases have dominated your life, your recovery must now become a priority. A recovery program consists of taking active steps. Merely abstaining from chemicals or waiting until your major depression goes away will guarantee continued unhappiness and problems in living. Recovery is not a matter of what you won't do but what you will do.

## Eating Right

Various biochemical imbalances are typical of coexisting chemical dependency and major depression. Much of this is due to the disease processes themselves. Abuse of addictive chemicals is associated with negative physiological changes in the brain. Serious depression is also associated with problematic changes in brain chemistry. In addition, those of us who are ill from these disorders often do not have a healthy diet. Maintaining good nutrition is helpful. When you follow a healthy food plan—appropriate amounts of the basic food groups at regular intervals—your physical health and, in turn, your emotional health will improve.

## Support from Others

Attending Twelve Step meetings such as Alcoholics Anonymous (AA), Narcotics Anonymous (NA), or Emotions Anonymous (EA) will serve as a key support in your efforts to stay clean and sober and to deal with your depression. At meetings you can hear others share their experience, strength, and hope. You can experience fellowship with others who have struggled and are still struggling with many of the same issues you face. Members are likely to give you supportive comments after the meeting and agree to give you their phone numbers so you can call them. You can talk honestly in the meetings about your problems and your feelings and about your efforts to recover without fear of judgment, ridicule, or criticism.

The open, caring, and nonjudgmental atmosphere of Twelve Step meetings will help you combat your feelings of being bad and shameful and help you practice expressing your thoughts and feelings directly. You will find laughter in these rooms. You will learn to take yoursef less seriously and enjoy each day as it comes. Most communities have different groups meeting at different times so that you will always have a place to go for support and can find a meeting that suits your needs. Attending meetings several times will also help you get more comfortable with this form of support.

Besides this general support, you can also find a sponsor. A sponsor is a member of a Twelve Step group who acts as a personal mentor and guide. A sponsor will help you learn about Twelve Step programs and support you during those tough times when you think you are alone and nobody understands how you feel. Finding a sponsor who accepts your psychiatric disorders and the potential use of medication is important. Explore your potential sponsor's feelings about this and ask whether he or she might be willing to work with you and understand that your recovery includes much.

## Getting Active

Getting into action can be difficult when you're depressed. The idea "I'll do that when I feel better," however, can actually make things worse. Pushing yourself to get active often improves feelings and thinking. The AA slogans "Fake it 'til you make it" and "Act as if" express well the goal and the impact of doing more to feel better. You may not feel like going to an AA meeting but chances are you will feel better once you do.

Being with others and doing fun things, including those associated with AA or NA, can help alleviate your depression as well as strengthen your sobriety program. Besides attending meetings, going out for coffee with group members after meetings offers you an opportunity to make new, sober friends. Attending any of the Twelve Step functions such as potlucks, bingo games, and clean and sober dances are helpful as well. Volunteering to help make coffee for a meeting or to set up chairs can help you interact with others and feel more a part of the group. Reach out a hand and introduce yourself. You will be surprised at how others will respond to this gesture.

Some form of physical activity is also beneficial. Going bowling, taking a brisk walk, or riding a bicycle will help you feel better and provide alternatives to drinking and using. Physical activities build self-esteem and often get you involved with others. They even help repair the altered brain chemistry associated with your two diseases and promote a sense of well-being.

## Thinking Constructively

Alcohol and drug abuse distort your thinking by causing denial and other negative attitudes. If you believe that fourteen citations for drunk driving represent a problem with the way you drive or if you blame your "nagging" spouse for your drinking problem, you are in denial.

Your depression also distorts your thinking. You may develop a view of yourself, the world, and the future that is so negative that you think nothing good ever happens. You may also think, *Everything is awful . . . Things always are and always will be terrible . . . It's all my fault.* These are common themes in depressed thinking. People who are depressed may remember only the bad things, discount positive feedback, and blame themselves for all the things they should have done or failed to do absolutely perfectly. A double dose of this alcoholic and depressive thinking can block your acceptance of your diseases and keep you from working a program that is likely to lead to recovery. This is stinking thinking. Put your thoughts into helping others.

## Working a Twelve Step Program

Working the Twelve Steps of Alcoholics Anonymous[*] is a key part of a recovery program and can combat negative thinking. Persons familiar with recovery often refer to the Twelve Steps as a "design for living." Not only can Twelve Step work help you maintain a chemically free life but it can also help you cope with the stresses and problems that life puts in your path. Of course, no one expects you to do Twelve Steps in twelve days. We all work at our own pace, one day at a time.

Step One of the Twelve Steps of Alcoholics Anonymous ("We admitted we were powerless over alcohol[and drugs]—that our lives had become unmanageable") can help you recognize that you are powerless not only over your drinking and using but also over your major depression. Attempting to control your chemical use and depression won't work. Major depression, like chemical dependency and other diseases, is not a matter of willpower alone. Physical, social, and legal problems due to chemical use signal unmanageability. Sleep and appetite disturbances, inability to perform daily activities, and a black, suicidal mood also indicate unmanageability. A complete First Step can help you acknowledge the fact that you have two illnesses and empower you to work a recovery program that is likely to be more effective than a willpower-only approach.

Steps Two and Three ("Came to believe that a Power greater than ourselves could restore us to sanity" and "Made a decision to turn our will and our lives over to the care of God *as we understood Him*") can give you the strength you need to reach out for help and have faith that things will get better. Steps Four and Five can help you get a realistic perspective on your shortcomings

---

[*] The complete Twelve Steps of Alcoholics Anonymous appear at the end of this pamphlet, on page 39.

(both real and those induced by the depression) and help you forgive yourself. The rest of the Steps will help you prevent relapse and promote continued recovery and growth through attitudes that emphasize acceptance, faith, honesty, true humility, and an openness to others.

You need to go to meetings even when you feel ugly, fat, and lonely. Go anyway. Members of Twelve Step groups commonly use certain phrases to express helpful ways to view themselves and the world. Phrases like "sick getting well, not bad getting good," "one day at a time," and "first things first" are examples. More phrases appear on page 24. Saying these slogans to yourself when you feel emotionally stuck or beaten will help you cultivate acceptance and serenity and combat distorted ideas or thinking. You can also schedule a review of this list once or twice a day and focus on a phrase that seems particularly relevant to your situation at that moment. At first this might seem artificial and without meaning, but with repetition and practice you are likely to experience a slow but sure change in your thinking that will promote your recovery and help you feel better.

## Getting Psychotherapy

A useful component of a recovery program for both of your disorders is psychotherapy with a qualified professional. A psychotherapist can support you, help you organize a recovery plan, teach you new ways to handle self-defeating actions and thoughts, and help you work through intense feelings. It's recommended that you look for a licensed or board-certified mental health professional such as a psychiatrist, psychologist, social worker, or chemical dependency counselor. Also, look for a professional with expertise in both mental health and chemical dependency, someone you feel you can trust and with whom you can develop a working relationship.

In your first session with your therapist, be sure to ask whether he or she has expertise in both addiction recovery as well as depression; psychotherapy alone is no substitute for other recovery components but is an important complement to your recovery work.

## Medication

Taking antidepressant medication can be a vital part of your treatment and recovery from major depression. One study showed that 40 percent of AA members had taken antidepressants at one time or another. Using antidepressant medication as a recovering person is so crucial and so controversial that the next section is devoted to this matter.

## Jack's Story

Jack had been around AA meetings off and on for the last five years. He found that he had frequent slips and had difficulty putting together more than ninety days of sobriety.

Jack really wanted sobriety, but at times he suffered from such dark moods that drinking or suicide seemed to be his only options. Jack chose to drink. On more than one occasion, however, Jack had seriously contemplated suicide. Once Jack had gone to a psychiatrist. He was drinking heavily at the time and didn't feel he got much out of therapy. Jack had always had trouble with depression, even before he started drinking. His father took his own life after fighting periods of depression.

Following Jack's last relapse, he decided maybe this time he would get into a treatment program. In treatment Jack saw a psychiatrist who diagnosed his problems as both alcoholism and depression. After treatment for alcoholism, Jack continued to have trouble sleeping and felt irritable and depressed. He returned to the psychiatrist he had seen at the treatment center and at sixty days of sobriety, Jack began taking antidepressant medication as prescribed by his doctor. After several weeks, Jack's moods improved and he began to get more out of his Twelve Step meetings. Jack came to hope that the program could work for him after all.

## Summary

1. The person with the dual disorders of chemical dependency and major depression can work a combined recovery program that has elements that address both disorders at the same time.

2. The key goals of a combined approach are accepting both diseases, abstaining from addictive chemicals, and working an active recovery program.

3. Important elements of a combined recovery program include

   - remaining abstinent

   - maintaining proper nutrition

   - attending Twelve Step meetings and getting a sponsor

   - engaging in social, recreational, and physical activities

   - working the Twelve Steps and using the recovery slogans to learn new ways of thinking

   - seeing a qualified therapist for psychotherapy

   - taking antidepressant medication

   - establishing strong spiritual practices

# TWELVE STEP SLOGANS

- Easy does it
- This, too, shall pass
- One day at a time
- First things first
- Turn it over
- Just for today
- Surrender
- More will be revealed
- You're right where you're supposed to be
- Fake it 'til you make it
- You're better than you think you are
- The paralysis of analysis
- Progress not perfection
- Let go and let God
- Stinking thinking
- Only one drink away from a drunk
- Powerless over people, places, and things
- Keep it simple
- God works through people
- Live in the solution not the problem
- Live life on life's terms
- Live in today
- Thy will, not mine
- If you don't take that first drink, you can't get drunk
- One drink is too many, but a thousand are not enough
- Live and let live

# THREE

# ANTIDEPRESSANT MEDICATION

Major depression is a disease and antidepressant medication often can be very helpful in recovering. Medications can help with your depressed mood, loss of pleasure, and problems with sleeping and eating. It's hard to have the energy to work your program when you aren't sleeping or giving your body its required nourishment. Taking antidepressant medication complements other recovery strategies such as psychotherapy and Twelve Step meetings, working the Steps, getting a sponsor, and reading the Big Book. Previously discussed strategies addressed your negative thinking, decreased activity level, and the interpersonal problems that stem from major depression. But complete recovery demands a comprehensive approach that may include medication.

Antidepressant medication is especially helpful for dealing with severe, persistent depression. Persistent depression can last week after week, even month after month, and can occur repeatedly. Persons suffering from severe depression may have begun to find absolutely nothing pleasurable in life and have serious difficulty carrying out even the basic activities of daily living. They may experience deep feelings of worthlessness and guilt.

People who are seriously depressed may not feel better, even briefly, if something good happens. They may find themselves especially depressed in the morning. They may discover that they are waking up several hours earlier than usual and find that they cannot fall back to sleep. They may have little or no appetite and lose substantial amounts of weight. Or they may find themselves in a cycle of compulsive overeating, trying to nurture themselves with food. You may require antidepressant medication as part of your recovery program if you suffer from severe depression. Antidepressants are not addictive or mood-altering. They are similar to taking antibiotics for a bacteria. Antidepressants, however, treat a lack of serotonin in the brain gradually, until you notice several weeks later how much you have improved.

Medical professionals use a variety of medications to treat major depression. They prescribe according to your symptoms and consider any other medical conditions you might have. Always consult a psychiatrist or qualified medical practitioner when you are considering the use of medication, and be sure to tell that person that you are in recovery from addiction.

## Medications and Side Effects

Antidepressant medications do have some limitations. They can take two to six weeks to work, which can seem forever when you're suffering from major depression. Always ask your physician to discuss possible side effects with you prior to your taking any medication.

Support from your family, friends, doctor, and sponsor can help you get through the several weeks it may require before the medication becomes effective. Working with you, your doctor can discover the dose of medication that is effective yet minimizes side effects. You may want to ask your sponsor or support person to go with you when you discuss medication with your physician. He or she can remind you to ask questions and support you if another person in recovery should question your use of medications. In many Twelve Step meetings, however, you will find that 35 to 40 percent of those in the meeting are using or have used antidepressants as a recovery tool.

## Special Concerns for People
## Who Are Chemically Dependent

Several issues confront the person recovering from chemical dependency who is considering the use of antidepressant medication. Recovery requires abstinence from mood-altering chemicals. Antidepressant medications are not considered drugs of abuse. I have never been invited to a Prozac party!

Remember that you have coexisting disorders, the disease of major depression and the disease of addiction. Medication can be an important and even crucial part of your treatment and recovery. Make a distinction between a drug that you abuse and a medication that you take for a disease. Consider that addictive substances disrupt body chemistry but that medication repairs neurochemistry.

## Beware of Tranquilizers

Potentially addictive medications are occasionally offered to treat symptoms of depression. Known as tranquilizers, these include medications such as Xanax and Valium, which are based on benzodiazepine. Some medications, such as Limbitrol, combine a tranquilizer with an antidepressant. These are addictive substances. Remember, *you* must guard your own recovery. Make it clear to your doctor that you do not want any addictive medicine, which would cause relapse. At the same time, rest assured that antidepressant medications designed specifically for major depression have little abuse potential and are not addictive.

Remember to take your medication only as prescribed. Always consult your physician about a change in dose; never just stop taking your medication. Stopping some antidepressant medications can cause rebound problems such as nausea, nightmares, or agitation. Don't get caught in the trap of thinking, *I feel fine now, so obviously I don't need the medication anymore.* Your medication is very likely part of what is helping you feel better!

Maintain your motivation by seeking support from others. There are special Twelve Step meetings for people on medication and for those who have dual disorders. Discuss your concerns with your physician and sponsor. Remember, too, that medication, like other parts of your recovery, is a one-day-at-a-time proposition.

## Susan's Story

Susan had been attending Twelve Step recovery meetings for four years when her mother died. She had never been close to her mother, so although she was sad about the loss, she took things one day at a time. About a year after her mother's death, Susan gave birth to a healthy baby girl. Susan and her husband were proud of the new addition to their family. But after the birth of her baby, Susan found herself thinking a lot about her own mother. She found it more and more difficult to sleep at night and when she did sleep, she would wake after only two hours. She also began to put on weight. Instead of the expected weight loss after delivery, Susan found her weight increasing. Feeling fat added to Susan's increasingly hopeless state of mind. Although she enjoyed her Twelve Step meetings and felt fine while there, as soon as she got home, feelings of great sadness would engulf her.

Susan discussed her feelings with a friend in the program, who suggested that Susan see a psychiatrist for therapy and discuss the possibility of antidepressant medication. Susan called the psychiatrist recommended by her friend and began both therapy and medication. At first Susan felt the antidepressants weren't helping much. But after about a week, she began sleeping through the night. By the time she had been taking the medication for a month, she noticed she'd stopped overeating and was starting to feel better. Susan continued in therapy for more than a year. During this time she was able to work through feelings of anger toward her mother and to grieve her death. Susan stayed on medication for only six months. She now enjoys the benefits of her Twelve Step program outside of meetings and has found the serenity and peace of mind she once thought impossible to achieve. The promises of the "Big Book" of Alcoholics Anonymous are coming true in Susan's life.

## Summary

1. Antidepressant medication is a powerful tool for recovery from the disease of major depression.

2. Tranquilizers, which are sometimes used for treating depression, are addictive and will lead to relapse.

3. Persons with the disease of chemical dependency can use antidepressant medication, designed specifically to treat depression, without risk to their recovery.

# CONCLUSION

Hopefully, you now recognize that you suffer from two diseases: addiction and depression.

We may not be responsible for our diseases and the problems they bring to our lives. We are responsible, however, for finding solutions to these problems.

Working a combined program of recovery can help guide you out of your problems and into solutions, one day at a time. *H*onesty, *O*penness, and *W*illingness are the HOW in how recovery works. By being honest, open, and willing, you are available to hear from a qualified professional if your sadness is part of unresolved grief or symptoms of major depression. The quality that living sobriety offers can be yours.

# APPENDIX A

# COMING TO KNOW YOUR DISORDERS

Use this worksheet to help apply the information in this pamphlet to your life. After reading the pamphlet, take some time to write down your answers for each of the following items. You may also wish to review your answers with your sponsor, your therapist, a friend, or an appropriate family member.

1. Write down at least five signs or problems that indicate that you suffer from the disease of chemical dependency.

_____

_____

_____

_____

_____

_____

2. Write down at least five signs or problems that indicate that you suffer from the disease of major depression.

_____

_____

_____

_____

_____

_____

3. Explain why you are "sick getting well," not "bad getting good" and why you are not responsible for having the diseases of chemical dependency and major depression.

_____

_____

_____

_____

_____

_____

4. List any major reservations you have about accepting your two diseases. For each reservation, list one thing you could think or do to deal with this reservation.

_____

_____

_____

_____

_____

5. List any major roadblocks that might stop you from making active recovery a priority in your life. Consider such obstacles as money and time, an unsupportive spouse, and your own attitudes (for example, you don't believe recovery will make a difference). For each roadblock, list a possible solution.

_____

_____

_____

_____

_____

_____

_____

_____

_____

6. Discuss why abstinence from alcohol and drugs is necessary for your recovery from both disorders.

_____

_____

_____

_____

_____

_____

_____

_____

7. List at least three things you could do to improve the quality of your recovery from chemical dependency, as well as your major depression.

_____

_____

_____

_____

_____

8. Describe any concerns you may have about taking antidepressant medication. Share these concerns with your doctor and sponsor. Being Honest, Open, and Willing are the keys.

_____

_____

_____

_____

_____

_____

9. Describe several ways that professional counseling or therapy could help your recovery.

_____

_____

_____

_____

_____

_____

10. List three "stinking thinking," or depressive thinking, patterns that are in your way. (Example: "Nothing will ever improve.")

_____

_____

_____

_____

_____

11. Take the three items in question 10 and reframe them in a positive light. (Example: "Nothing will ever change" becomes "One step at a time, one day at a time, I am happier than yesterday.")

_____

_____

_____

_____

_____

_____

# THE TWELVE STEPS
# OF ALCOHOLICS
# ANONYMOUS*

1. We admitted we were powerless over alcohol—that our lives had become unmanageable.

2. Came to believe that a Power greater than ourselves could restore us to sanity.

3. Made a decision to turn our will and our lives over to the care of God *as we understood Him.*

4. Made a searching and fearless moral inventory of ourselves.

5. Admitted to God, to ourselves, and to another human being the exact nature of our wrongs.

6. Were entirely ready to have God remove all these defects of character.

7. Humbly asked Him to remove our shortcomings.

8. Made a list of all persons we had harmed, and became willing to make amends to them all.

---

* The Twelve Steps of AA are reprinted from *Alcoholics Anonymous,* 3d ed., published by AA World Services, Inc., New York, N.Y., 59–60. Reprinted with permission from AA World Services, Inc. (See editor's note on copyright page.)

9. Made direct amends to such people wherever possible, except when to do so would injure them or others.

10. Continued to take personal inventory and when we were wrong promptly admitted it.

11. Sought through prayer and meditation to improve our conscious contact with God *as we understood Him,* praying only for knowledge of His will for us and the power to carry that out.

12. Having had a spiritual awakening as the result of these steps, we tried to carry this message to alcoholics, and to practice these principles in all our affairs.